This Book Belongs To

_____

A Communion of the Heart

Written by: Pamela Patnode

Illustrated by: Austin Duncan

Philomena Press
providing faithful resources for faith-filled families

Philomena Press LLC
6569 Garland Lane N.
Minneapolis, MN 55311

All Bible quotations and citations come from the Catholic Study Bible: New
American Bible.

To my Godchildren:
Max R., Jurrien, Andrew, and Max B.
I love you!

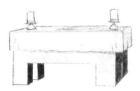

Chapter One
Did You See That?

"Did you see that guy during Communion?" asked Grace's older brother, J.P.

Eight-year-old Grace O'Malley enjoyed these car rides with her family. With four older siblings who were active in many activities, it was rare to find the entire family all together in one vehicle. Often some were in one car driving to one set of activities, while others headed in a different direction for their own practices, games, lessons, and meetings. Mass, however, was a top priority for the family and they made every effort to attend the Sunday Celebration together.

Grace's family loved the parish community of St. John's Catholic Church. As active members of the parish, Grace felt at home among the people and surroundings of St. John's. Not only did Grace's family attend Mass on Sundays, but they also participated in many church activities throughout the week. This familiarity with St. John's caused Grace and her siblings to notice the newcomer and watch with curiosity and interest as the stranger received the Eucharist.

"Do you mean the man who received Communion while kneeling on both knees?" questioned the O'Malley's middle child, Lorraine.

"I saw him," answered nine-year-old Kathleen. "I thought he looked like he was from a different country."

"I saw him, too" replied Grace. "Why did he receive communion like that?"

"I think he was just being really reverent," responded thirteen-year-old Marie.

"I've never seen anyone do that before," exclaimed Lorraine.

"Oh I have," stated J.P. "Marie's right. That guy was just being reverent."

"What's reverent?" asked Grace.

"It means that you're trying to show a lot of respect for Jesus," explained Marie.

Impressed, Grace admired her brother and older sister. She was surprised that they had seen someone receive Communion like that before and that they understood why.

"Mom," asked a concerned Lorraine, "Should we be receiving Communion on our knees? I mean, does Jesus think we're not reverent if we receive the Eucharist while standing? Does anyone in our country receive Communion that way?"

"When I made my First Communion," interrupted Kathleen, "our Faith Formation director told us to stand up and either use one of our hands to make a 'throne' for Jesus, or to receive the Consecrated Host on our tongue. No one ever told me I was supposed to kneel on both knees to receive Him."

"Yeah!" interjected Lorraine. "And what about Grandma? She wouldn't be able to kneel. What should she do?"

"Hold on, hold on everyone," replied their Mom. "There's no need to worry about Grandma. Your Faith Formation instructors gave you good instructions for the way we should be receiving Christ in Holy Communion.

As far as the visitor we saw today, to tell you the truth, I've seen people receive the Eucharist using many different postures. Like you, I've seen people receive our Lord while standing, making one of their hands a 'throne' as you mentioned Kathleen, as well as on the tongue. I've seen people genuflect before receiving our Lord and I've seen people kneel as the gentleman did today at Mass. And yet, I've never actually asked anyone why they receive Communion using the method that they choose. I believe J.P. and Marie are right in suggesting that the man today was simply expressing his love and humility before Christ. But, I think it would be fun to learn more about this. The gestures we use when we worship are very important and are steeped in meaningful tradition. Let's look into this further and see what we can learn."

J.P. and Marie exchanged smirks and rolled their eyes. They were used to their mother always wanting to uncover the answers to religious questions. Grace, however, wanted to know more. Her very own First Holy

Communion was fast approaching and she wanted to know the right way to do it. *What if St. John's is doing it wrong?* worried Grace. *Does Jesus prefer that we receive Holy Communion a certain way? What is the right way to receive Communion?*

Chapter Two
A Letter to the Pope

Grace awoke the next morning and hastily scampered out of bed. She lifted the shade and eagerly peered out of the window.

"Did it snow?" asked her sister, Kathleen.

"Yes!" Grace joyfully exclaimed.

"A lot?" asked Kathleen, hope rising within her.

"It looks like a lot," replied Grace.

"Good morning, girls," announced their mother. "Well, you got your wish. Everything is closed today. Can you believe it? We got a lot of snow last night, and they're predicting more snow later today."

"Yes! Yes! Yes!" cheered Grace while pumping her fist.

"Hooray!" exclaimed Kathleen as she jumped up and down upon her bed, bursting with joy.

"You may go back to sleep if you like," suggested their mom who grinned broadly.

"No way!" chorused Grace and Kathleen together. "Let's get dressed and go out to play in the snow!" they cheered.

"Mom, can I call Anna and ask her to play with us?" asked Grace.

Grace's best friend Anna lived just a few houses away from the O'Malley's. The two families shared a park behind their houses and spent many hours playing together at this park.

"Yes," answered their Mother. "However, I want you to pick up your room, get dressed, and eat breakfast before you head outside. Why don't you ask Anna to meet you at the park in an hour?"

Pure joy filled the day as Grace, her siblings, and their friends built snowmen, raced in sleds, threw snowballs, and delighted in the

unexpected gift of freedom from school and schedules.

At dinner, Grace's family talked excitedly about the day and their hopes for another snowstorm. After hearing from each of his children about the fun activities that filled their day, Grace's dad turned to their mother and asked, "What did you do today, honey?"

Her dad winked as he said this and his eyes twinkled. "Were you out on a sled?"

Smiling, Grace's mom replied, "Well, although I was tempted to sneak outside and throw a few well aimed snowballs, in the end, I decided to stay inside. Actually, I started doing some research on the question we talked about yesterday after Mass. I'm learning some interesting things about the gestures we use in our Catholic faith. In fact, here's something that you kids might find to be of interest. Do any of you know why we genuflect in church?"

"I don't even know what genuflect means," replied Grace.

"It's when you bend one knee down before

entering the pew," replied Lorraine.

"That's right, Lorraine," replied their mother. "I learned something interesting about the history of this gesture. Back in Roman times, more than 2,000 years ago, it was common for people to genuflect before the Emperor, or their local ruler. This gesture indicated that the person who knelt acknowledged the leader as their superior and their Lord. The Bible also mentions in several places how people knelt when praying to God.

"Well," their mom continued, "Christians adopted this action. As Christians, however, we do not genuflect before a government leader. Rather, we kneel before Christ, who we know is

present in our Church. Jesus, in the humble form of the Consecrated Host, might be in the tabernacle, in the monstrance, or on the altar during Mass. As Catholics, we acknowledge that Christ alone is our King of Kings and Lord of Lords. Therefore, we genuflect before Him. Isn't that interesting?"

"What's that thing you said?" asked Grace. "You said Jesus might be in the tabernacle or the *monster*?"

"Not 'monster', goofball," replied J.P. "It's called a *monstrance*. A monstrance is the beautiful holder used for the Consecrated Host. It's what we see in the adoration chapel."

Embarrassed, Grace hung her head while her siblings laughed and repeated the word 'monster'. *How am I supposed to know all of this stuff anyway?* Grace wondered. *I'm only eight. I bet they didn't know what a Monstrance was when they were eight. Sometimes it's hard being the youngest.*

"That's enough," their mother reprimanded. "Grace, I'm glad you asked that question. There are a lot of grown-ups who have not heard of that word, so you shouldn't feel embarrassed. And, I don't know about all of you, but I thought it was interesting to learn about the history of genuflecting. I plan to do more research about other gestures we use."

"Why do you have to do research?" asked Lorraine. "Can't you just ask Father Duncan to tell you why we do these things and how we should receive Communion?"

"Or," suggested Marie, "you could ask the Archbishop. He is, after all, Father Duncan's boss. I bet he'd know the best way to receive Communion."

"I think we should ask the Pope!" proposed Grace excitedly.

"Yeah! Wouldn't that be cool?" exclaimed Kathleen with a certain sense of awe.

"You can't ask the Pope," stated J.P. "What are you going to do, just call him up on the phone?"

"No, I'm not going to call him," Grace retorted angrily. "But I can write him a letter."

"Grace," replied J.P. "You're too little to understand. The Pope is a busy guy. He doesn't have time to answer silly questions and write back to eight-year-old kids."

"It's not a silly question!" Grace exclaimed, tears of fury forming in her eyes.

"Hold on, you two," interjected their mom.

"Grace, you're right. Asking how to receive Communion is not a silly question. It's actually a very important question. In fact, it's probably a question more people should be asking."

"Yeah, but seriously, Mom," contested J.P. "The Pope? We don't need to ask the Pope to find out the answer."

"Well, you're right, J.P. There are other ways to find the answer to this question. We can start by asking Father Duncan. He may not be the Pope, but he is a very good and holy priest. We can also look into the *Catechism of the Catholic Church*. The *Catechism* explains in great detail all aspects of our Catholic Christian faith. In addition, I have some excellent books about Catholic practices that could provide additional information."

"So I can't write to the Pope?" Grace asked with obvious disappointment.

"You can write to him, but he may not write back," stated her brother.

"But he just might," countered Grace with determination.

"That's right," replied her mom. "I imagine that the Pope probably gets a lot of mail. I don't know if he can answer every letter he receives. But if you want to write to him, I think you should. I'll help you find the mailing address."

*　　*　　*

That night, in her room, Grace took out a sheet of paper and a pencil. In her best handwriting, she carefully wrote to the Pope. At first, Grace wasn't exactly sure what to say. She wasn't even sure how she should start the letter. Simply writing, "Dear Pope" didn't seem quite right. After thinking about it for a while, she decided to write, "Dear Holy Father Pope Francis." Grace hoped that would be respectful. Then she continued:

Dear Holy Father Pope Francis,
　Hello! My name is Grace O'Malley. I am eight years old and am the youngest child in my family. I will be making

my First Holy Communion this Spring and I really want to do it the right way. Last Sunday at church, we saw a man receive the Eucharist on his knees. I had never seen anyone do that before. Is that the best way to receive Jesus? I love Jesus and I want to make sure I receive Communion the right way. My sister said the man was being reverent. I want to be reverent too. I figured you are pretty close to Jesus and would probably know the answer to this question. What, Pope Francis, is the best way to receive Holy Communion? Please write back.

Thank you.

Most sincerely,

Grace O'Malley

Chapter Three
Isn't it Just a Symbol?

The weeks passed quickly as spring fought desperately to overcome winter. Finally, spring seemed to gain the advantage. The weather warmed, the snow began to melt, and a few birds could be heard chirping as the sun rose each day.

The O'Malley family busily made

preparations for Easter and Grace's first Holy Communion, which was scheduled for the Sunday after Easter, Divine Mercy Sunday. Everyone seemed to be excited about the upcoming events. Everyone, that is, except Grace. Two things bothered her. First, she had not received any mail from the Pope. Day after day, she went to the mail box with hopeful anticipation. And, day after day, she walked slowly back to her house empty-handed. *Maybe J.P. was right,* she thought. *I guess the Pope is too busy. He probably doesn't have time to write back to me.* The second thing that bothered her was a comment that her friend

Anna had made.

The day before, Anna had invited Grace to spend the night. Grace had to decline the invitation because her mother wanted to go dress shopping. Grace needed a white dress for her First Eucharist. Anna had been excited to hear the details of what the dress might look like. Anna was not Catholic. At Anna's church they celebrated the Last Supper differently. It was not a part of their weekly worship services. Anna had listened intently as Grace explained what her dress and First Communion Mass would be like. Then Grace confided in Anna her concerns about receiving the Sacred Host correctly.

"I'm not sure if I should genuflect, kneel, or stand up to receive it," admitted Grace. "My mom is doing some research about it, and she told me not to worry. She said I could stand

like everyone at our church typically does. But," Grace added, "I'm not so sure."

"Wow," Anna had replied. "You really do things differently at your church. It sounds like you guys make a big deal out of communion. Why?"

"Well," Grace had explained, "I guess it's

because the Communion is Jesus, and we should always make a big deal about Jesus."

"What do you mean by saying it is Jesus?" Anna had questioned. "How can a piece of bread and some wine be Jesus? That's weird. Does it actually look like Jesus?"

"Well, no," stammered Grace. "Um, I guess I don't really know. I've just always been told that during the Mass the bread and wine change into the actual body and blood of Jesus."

"Can you actually see Jesus when it changes?"

"No, not exactly," Grace had admitted.

"Huh," Anna had responded. "I don't think I understand. At my church we just call the communion a *symbol* of Christ's last supper. We don't worry about kneeling or standing or wearing white dresses for a symbol. I wish I could help you but I don't know what to say. Well, anyway, I'd still like to see your dress when you get it. Maybe you can sleep over next week."

*   *   *

As Grace and her mother drove to the store for the First Communion dress, Grace stared out the car window, lost in thought. Anna's comment about Holy Communion being just a symbol of Jesus bothered her. *If Anna was right,* Grace considered, *if the Holy Communion is just a symbol and not actually Christ, well then we didn't need to worry about kneeling or genuflecting or anything else.*

Grace determined to look more closely at Mass on Sunday. Maybe the Sacred Host did actually resemble Christ, and Grace had never noticed it before. She intended to sit as near to the altar as possible and closely examine

the communion wafer. Grace figured that she wouldn't be allowed to use binoculars, but she was going to do everything she could to see the Sacred Host as precisely as possible. She felt like a detective, and this was one mystery she intended to solve.

Chapter Four
Can You See Jesus?

The next morning, Grace awoke early and quickly got dressed for Mass. Sunday mornings always involved a flurry of activity in the O'Malley home as the seven members of the family tried to get ready and out of the house on time. The shower ran constantly, hair dryers blew, people shouted and pillaged through laundry baskets in search of dress pants and lost socks. Although the O'Malley's went to Mass every week, and the Mass times rarely changed, the effort to actually get out of the house well groomed and on time proved a challenge.

Grace, however, was on a mission. She determined that their family would sit in the very front row, with an excellent view of the altar. Therefore, she climbed into the car as soon as she was prepared for Mass, and waited with growing impatience for the rest of her family to join her.

Finally, the car was fully loaded with seven passengers, and they headed off to St. John's. While driving, their father commented on some information that he had recently uncovered.

"Your mom's research inspired me to do a little of my own. Anyone interested in knowing why we make the Sign of the Cross?" he asked.

"Dad, isn't it weird that you and mom get so much enjoyment out of learning about this stuff?" asked Marie. "I don't think any of my friends' parents are reading Catholic encyclopedias in their down time."

"Oh, I don't know," answered their father. "I think you'd be surprised. Many of our

friends do find it interesting to learn about their faith. I think the more we understand what we're doing and saying, the more meaning it will hold for us. If we are just going through the motions with no understanding of their beautiful significance, then our faith can seem empty."

"Well, are you going to tell us what it

means?" asked Kathleen.

"Yes," replied their father smiling. "According to some books I've been reading, I learned that Christians started marking themselves with the Sign of the Cross as early as the second century. The Sign of the Cross is truly significant to us as Christians. Two important beliefs it represents include the Holy Trinity and Christ's saving act upon the cross.

"As far as the Holy Trinity goes, when we cross ourselves, we are publicly acknowledging our belief in the Father, the Son, and the Holy Spirit. In addition, when we make the Sign of the Cross, we recall Jesus' passion, death, and resurrection. We are reminded that it is through the cross that Jesus redeemed us. Pretty interesting isn't it? To think that people have been making the Sign of the Cross for nearly 2,000 years is remarkable."

"That is interesting," their mother agreed. "And, now, since we're pulling into the parking lot, we should get ourselves ready for Mass."

As her dad drove up to the front door of St. John's, Grace nearly leapt out of the vehicle. She bolted inside and made a straight-line dash for the front row. Surprised by her haste, Grace's family followed and filed into the pew.

Mass progressed as usual, although to Grace it seemed to take longer. She waited impatiently for the Consecration, the moment during Mass when, through the words and prayers of the priest, acting together with the Holy Spirit, the bread and wine turn into the real Body and Blood of Jesus. Grace fidgeted throughout the readings and the homily, barely able to contain her anticipation.

Finally, the moment arrived. The priest spoke the words and elevated the Host, "This is my Body . . ." he said. As he spoke, Grace leaned forward, straining her eyes to examine the Sacred Bread. While the congregation knelt, Grace slowly rose from her knees. Her eyes were wide and fixed on the Eucharist. Without realizing it, she tiptoed on the kneeler, leaning so far forward that she lost her balance and with a loud noise nearly toppled over. Her mother grabbed her arm just in time. As she resumed her kneeling position, her cheeks burned with embarrassment. Everyone in her family looked at her, wondering what in the world she had been doing. Grace imagined that the rest of the church was looking at her as well. However, she was too embarrassed to look up, and kept her head down for the remainder of Mass.

"What the heck were you doing during Mass, Grace?" asked J.P. as soon as they were in the car.

"Yeah," chorused her sisters. "You almost fell out of the pew!"

Her siblings laughed while Grace sulked with shame and embarrassment. She did not answer their questions.

At home, Grace ran straight to her bedroom, shut the door, and then hid in her closet. While

crouching beneath a hanging bathrobe, Grace heard her mother enter her room and turn the handle on the closet door.

"Grace?" asked her mother.

"What?" responded Grace with angry tears.

"Are you okay?" questioned her mom.

"No," stated Grace. "All I was trying to do was to see Jesus. Anna told me that their church thinks communion is just a symbol of Jesus. When I told her that we believe it is actually the Body and Blood of Christ she asked if I could see Him. I wanted to try. Then, I almost fell out of the pew and now everyone thinks I'm a weirdo."

"Nobody thinks you're a weirdo, so don't worry about that. Did you see Jesus?" asked her mom.

"No. I looked really hard but I couldn't see Him. I wanted to see if the Host changes shape or Jesus' face appears on it or something. I couldn't see anything different about it. And then I almost fell, so I quit looking."

"Grace," replied her mother. "I think that what you did today at Mass was beautiful. Oh how I wish everyone tried as hard as you do to see Jesus. It can be difficult! I even have a hard time finding Jesus. I look for Him all over – in other people, in God's creation, in prayer, and in the Eucharist. And you know what? It can be very hard at times to see Him. I'm so very, very glad that you tried. And, I hope you'll keep trying. Don't ever stop looking for Jesus!"

"But is Holy Communion just a symbol? And if it's just a symbol, why do we make such a big deal about it?"

"That's an excellent question. Why don't we bring that question to Father Duncan and see what he has to say. In fact, we haven't had him over for dinner in a while. I'll call him to see when he can come. We can ask him while he's here."

*   *   *

A few days later, Father Duncan arrived at the O'Malley house to enjoy dinner, conversation, and a game of cards. Once dinner was over and the table had been cleared, Mrs. O'Malley asked Father Duncan if he could answer Grace's question before they started playing cards.

"Sure. I love Grace's questions!" exclaimed the jovial pastor. "I just hope you don't stump me. I'll do my best to answer whatever is on your mind."

Grace nervously looked around the table at her siblings and then she turned her attention to Father Duncan. Grace liked Father Duncan. He had been the pastor of St. John's for as long as she could remember. He was a good and holy priest who had a welcoming smile and an infectious laugh. With a small amount of nervous hesitation Grace began to speak.

"Father Duncan, at Mass last week I looked for Jesus in the Eucharist. I couldn't see Him. My friend Anna says that the Communion is just a symbol of Jesus and the Last Supper. Is that true? And if it really is Jesus, why can't I see Him?"

Father Duncan looked thoughtfully at

Grace. He also looked around at the others at the table. Pausing momentarily, Father Duncan asked, "J.P., can you please bring me a glass of milk?"

"Sure," replied Grace's brother. He rose from the table, filled a glass of milk, and brought it to the beloved priest.

"Grace," Father Duncan began, "there are many things in life that we ourselves can't see or taste or touch but that we have good reason to believe are really there. We take the word of those who have shown with scientific experiments that this is the way things are. For example, have you ever heard of calcium?"

"Yes," answered Grace.

"Where do we find calcium?" asked the

pastor.

"Well, in lots of places, like milk," replied Grace.

"That's right," answered Father Duncan. "Grace, how do you know there is calcium in milk? Can you see it?"

"Well, no," replied Grace. "I can't see it. But we learned about it in school."

"That's correct," said Father Duncan. "We can't see the calcium and we can't really taste it, either. But we know it's there. A lot of smart people like doctors and scientists have studied milk and have found through scientific experiments that calcium is really in the milk we drink. They have told us about this in textbooks and on the side of milk cartons. And we take the word of these educated people, even though we *ourselves* can't see or taste the calcium. We take them at their word because we understand that they are the experts in these matters and that if we ourselves had the ability and took the trouble to do the right experiments, we would see that what they told us is the way things really are. So, too, you hear a lot today about "dark matter and dark energy" which, according to the scientists' mathematical calculations, must make up most of the universe, and yet no one has ever seen it or felt it or knows exactly what it is."

Father Duncan took a sip of milk and then continued.

"In a similar way, you and I can't see it or feel it when the bread and wine are being changed in their substance into Christ's own body and blood. But we know that this is what is actually taking place in the Mass when the priest repeats the words that Our Lord Himself used at the Last Supper, the first Mass. We believe this because Christ is God, God the Son, the Second Person of the Blessed Trinity, and He has told us that this is what in fact took place at the Last Supper when He said these words. And He told the Apostles (and through them those who would continue their work down through the centuries) to keep on doing what He had just done. 'Do this in memory of Me' – to keep Christ's presence living in people's minds and hearts until He comes again at the very end of time.

"Since Christ is God, He can do whatever He chooses to do. Changing a little bit of bread and wine into His body and blood while leaving the outward appearance of bread and wine so that we could eat and drink it is no problem at all for the One through Whom the whole universe was made. And because Christ is God He always tells the truth; He will never deceive us. And so, with the needed help that He gives us when we try to do His will, the help that He gives us through the virtue of faith, we believe Him when He tells us: 'This is My body; this is the chalice of My blood.' If we take the word of scientific experts who only observe what is already there and who can and sometimes do make mistakes, all the more should we take as absolute truth the testimony of the Son of God. For God knows all things and can do all things, He is the all-powerful Lord of heaven and earth, and He always tells the truth. If we accept the testimony of men, the testimony of God is greater.

"Grace, let's look in the Bible and see what our Lord actually says about His own flesh and blood becoming truly the Bread of Eternal Life. As the pastor of St. John's Catholic Church, I always love to begin with St. John's Gospel. Can I see your Bible, Grace?"

Grace rose and retrieved the Bible from the

family room. She handed the Bible to Father Duncan, who opened it to the Gospel of John, chapter 6.

"Grace, I'd like to read you something from this book of the Bible. In John, chapter 6 beginning with verse 47, Jesus tells us:

Amen, amen, I say to you, whoever believes has eternal life. I am the bread of life. Your ancestors ate the manna in the desert, but they died; this is the bread that comes down from heaven so that one may eat of it and not die. I am the living bread that came down from heaven; whoever eats this bread will live forever; and the bread that I will give is my flesh for the life of the world.

"Grace, the Jewish people had a hard time

understanding these words of Jesus. The Bible tells us that they even argued about it. In John 6:52, the Bible says:

The Jews quarreled among themselves, saying: 'How can this man give us His flesh to eat?' Jesus said to them, 'Amen, amen I say to you, unless you eat the flesh of the Son of Man and drink His blood, you do not have life within you. Whoever eats my flesh and drinks my blood has eternal life, and I will raise him on the last day. My flesh is food indeed, and my blood is drink indeed. Whoever eats my flesh and drinks my blood remains in me and I in him.

"Grace, Jesus does not call the bread that He gives us just a symbol. You'll notice he does not say, 'Imagine if you will that this is a symbol of my body and blood.' No, He is very, very specific in saying numerous times that we must eat His flesh and drink His blood, that His flesh is food indeed, and His blood is drink, indeed.

"As I mentioned earlier, it was hard for the followers of Jesus to understand how He could give them His flesh to eat and His blood to drink. Some of them outright refused to believe His words. They walked away. Jesus let them go. He did not say, 'Wait a minute! Hold on! I don't mean this literally, I was just speaking in symbols. You misunderstood Me.'

No. Jesus did not say this. In fact, as some of the people were leaving Him, Jesus turned to Peter and the other Apostles and asked if they also intended to leave. Peter understood that following Jesus means believing in teachings that are sometimes difficult to understand. He understood that following Jesus takes faith, real faith. St. Peter responded to Jesus by saying, 'Lord, to whom shall we go? It is You who have the words of everlasting life. And we have believed and have come to know that You are the Holy One of God.'

"In other words, St. Peter was saying, 'We don't understand what You have said just now, but You are God, and if You say it's so, then we know it's true.'"

Grace sat back in her chair and considered what Father Duncan had said. It made sense. She looked up at Father Duncan and said with a smile "Thank you, Father."

"Can we play cards now?" asked Kathleen.

"You bet," replied the pastor.

Chapter Five
Grace's First Communion

Easter dawned in all its glory. The bright sunshine, buds upon trees, and greening grass helped to proclaim, not only the Earth's victory over winter, but also Christ's victory over Death. Indeed, the day was filled with tremendous joy. Grace's family attended Mass, hunted for Easter eggs and Easter baskets, and shared a special dinner with aunts, uncles, cousins, and grandparents. It was during this dinner when the conversation turned to Grace's upcoming First Holy Communion.

"I hear your dress is lovely," proclaimed Grace's grandmother. "May I see it?"

"Sure," replied Grace as she hustled toward her bedroom to fetch her beautiful outfit. She had a white dress, matching shoes, and a white ring of flowers that would rest on top of her head. Grace showed all of this off with great care and pride as her relatives "oohed" and "aahed".

"Oh, Grace," exclaimed her Grandmother. "I can hardly wait to see you in this dress. It is beautiful."

"Thank you, Grandma," replied Grace. Then she returned the dress to her room where it would be kept safe until the big day.

"I think it is truly special that the children will receive their First Communion on Divine Mercy Sunday," commented Grace's aunt.

"I agree," replied her mom.

"Did you hear about Grace's letter?" asked her sister Lorraine.

"What letter?" questioned their aunt.

"Lorraine, I'm not sure Grace wanted everyone to know about her letter. You should have asked her first before mentioning it," stated their mother.

"It's okay," replied Grace who had re-entered the room. "I wrote a letter to the Pope. My brother and sisters don't think he'll ever write back to me."

"Wow! A letter to the Pope," exclaimed their aunt. "I've never written to the Pope before. That's pretty exciting! What did you say?"

"Well," explained Grace, "I asked him how I should receive Communion. I want to make sure I'm receiving with reverence and I wanted to know if I should kneel or stand to receive the Host."

"That's a great question, Grace. Will you let me know if you do hear back from him?"

"Sure. But, it's been almost six weeks and I haven't heard anything yet. If I do, I'll let you know," Grace responded.

*   *   *

That night in bed, after saying prayers with her family, Grace held a silent conversation with Jesus. Privately, Grace prayed, "Hi, Jesus. I know you realize that I'll be making my First Communion a week from today. I still don't know the 'right' way to do it. My mom said I should do what our Faith Formation director

instructed us to do. Since I didn't hear back
from the Pope, I guess that's what I'll have to
do. I just hope you know I love you. Happy
Easter, Jesus."

*   *   *

After school on Friday, Grace's mom

recruited the children to help prepare the house for the First Communion celebration on Sunday. She needed their assistance with chores while she made preparations for the brunch they planned to have following the First Communion Mass. Lorraine was put in charge of dusting, J.P. vacuumed, Marie helped to fold laundry, and Kathleen picked up miscellaneous books and toys, and put them away.

"How can I help?" asked Grace.

"Let's see," her mom responded thoughtfully. "Can you empty the dishwasher for me? Oh, and why don't you go bring in the mail."

"Okay," responded Grace.

Carefully, she lifted the plates and glasses

from the dishwasher and put them away in the cupboards. After putting the forks, knives, and spoons in the silverware drawer, Grace headed in the direction of the mailbox.

Peering inside the postal container, Grace saw a number of materials – magazines and catalogs mixed with envelopes and flyers. She grabbed the stack of materials and returned to the house. As she put the mail down on the kitchen counter, something caught Grace's eye. It was an emblem that she had never seen before. Then she spotted the word "Vatican" on the envelope.

Heart racing, Grace called out, "Mom, come quick!"

Her mother hurried into the kitchen and promptly asked, "What is it, Honey?"

"Look!" Grace exclaimed, shoving the envelope into her mother's hands.

"Oh, Grace! This is from the Vatican!" Then her mother called out, "J.P., Marie, Lorraine, Kathleen, come quick. Look at what Grace received in the mail today!"

Grace's siblings joined her in the kitchen and looked on with surprise and admiration.

"Open it!" encouraged Kathleen.

"I will," stated Grace.

Her hands were shaking slightly as she gingerly opened the sealed envelope. Inside was a letter addressed to her. Grace began to read the letter silently until her siblings chorused excitedly, "Come on, read it out loud! What does it say?"

Grace carefully read the words aloud.

Dear Grace,

Thank you for your thoughtful letter. I am so happy to hear that you will be making your First Holy Communion. Not only am I happy for you, but I believe Jesus is happy, too. From your letter, I can tell that you are concerned about the best way to receive Communion. The gestures that we use to worship are very important. I'm glad that you recognize how important they are. When you receive

Holy Communion, Grace, I want you to focus on one thing. What you should focus on is your heart. The best posture we can offer to Jesus when receiving Him in the Eucharist is to present Him with an open heart. If we can open our hearts to receive Christ's love for us, and then be willing to share that love with others, we will be receiving Him in the best possible way. Your wonderful faith formation directors will show you how to kneel or stand, and any other important details about the liturgy. Follow their directions. And then, as you approach the Sacred Host, be certain to open your heart so that Christ can fill it with His love. God bless you my dear child.

With great love,
Francis

Grace, her mother, and her siblings stood in silence for a moment, absorbing the words of the Holy Father.

"Wow," replied J.P. "That's incredible. My little sister got a letter from the Pope."

"We should frame it," suggested Marie.

"Good idea," agreed their mom.

"Can I call dad at work and tell him?" asked Grace.

"Absolutely," replied her mother who reached for the phone and began punching in the numbers.

Grace spent the next hour making lots of phone calls. She called her dad, her aunt, her grandparents, and even her friend Anna. It was so exciting to have received a letter from the

Pope. She still couldn't quite believe it.

The following day, Saturday, Grace's mom went to the store and purchased a frame in which she could put the letter. Then, they found a place on Grace's bedroom wall upon which to hang the treasured keepsake.

That night, Grace had a hard time falling asleep. After many failed attempts, she decided to get up and talk to her mom. She walked down the hall into her parents' room where Grace could see that her mother's reading light was still on. Her dad was still downstairs. Grace's mom looked up from her book and smiled as her youngest child entered the room. Climbing into bed beside her mother, Grace said,

"I can't fall asleep. I'm too excited."

"I bet you are," replied her mother. "This has been a very exciting journey for you. Not many people can say that they've received a personal letter from the Pope. I'm proud of you, Grace. You put a lot of effort into finding the answers to your faith questions. I hope you will continue to ask questions and continue to seek the answers. Our Faith is so rich, and the more we learn, the more we realize there is to know. Don't ever quit learning Gracie. I love you."

With that, her mom kissed Grace on the top of her head.

"Now, however," continued her mom, "I think that you should go back to bed and close your eyes. Tomorrow is a big day. A letter from the Pope is certainly exciting, but nothing can compare to receiving the actual Body and Blood of our Lord. Go back to bed and try to get some sleep."

Grace went back to bed, closed her eyes,

and fell asleep with a smile upon her lips.

*   *   *

The next morning dawned gray and cloudy. As the family prepared to leave for Mass, some rays of sun could be seen trying to break through the dark clouds. Grace put on her dress with great care. Her mother took extra time arranging Grace's hair, placing the white flowered wreath just right upon her daughter's head.

During the car ride to Mass, it was decided that Grace would tell Father Duncan about the Pope's letter, although she would wait until after Mass to make mention of it. As they approached St. John's Catholic Church for the important

Sacrament, Grace's mom reflected, "Let's all be sure that we receive Holy Communion the way our Holy Father suggested, by opening our hearts to receive Christ's love."

As the Mass progressed, Grace was reminded of many things. She thought about Anna's comment and how she had almost fallen out of the pew in her effort to see Jesus. Grace thought about the dinner they shared with Father Duncan. She also thought about the Pope's letter. As she listened to Father Duncan's homily which talked about Christ's Divine Mercy, she realized that Jesus truly does love us. She was glad she could finally receive Him in Holy Communion.

At last the moment for her First Holy Communion arrived and Grace stepped in line with her parents. When Father Duncan said, "The Body of Christ," Grace's heart was nearly bursting with love and joy. She emphatically responded, "Amen!"

As she returned to her seat, Grace stole a glance out the window where the sun shone brightly. Filled with gratitude and love, Grace knelt with her family and privately prayed a heartfelt prayer, "Thank you, Jesus! I love you!"

Epilogue

Grace smiled up at her mother as her mom tucked her into bed that night.

"Mom," Grace asked. "Do I have to wait a whole week before making my second communion?"

Grace's mom smiled. "No, Darling. The beautiful thing about the Catholic Church is that we can receive Jesus in the Eucharist each and every day."

"Do some people really go to church every day?" asked Grace.

"Yes. Many people go every single day. I don't know if our family can go daily. However, we will continue to go every single Sunday. And, I think it would be a great idea to pick a day to attend a daily Mass. That would be a wonderful thing for our family to do."

"Thank you, Mommy. I can't wait to go to Communion again."

"We will, Darling. We will go again, and again, and again, and again and again – every week, every year. I'm so happy for you, Grace, and so proud of you. I love you."

"Thank you, Mommy, I love you, too."

As Grace's mom turned out the light and left the room, Grace said a silent prayer to Jesus, "Good night, Jesus. I love you, too!"

For More Information

This story gives just a small amount of information regarding the Catholic Church's teaching on the Sacrament of Holy Communion. To learn more, please see the resources listed below.

The Bible teaches us very clearly that the Holy Eucharist is indeed the Body and Blood of our Lord and Savior. Jesus chose His words very carefully when talking about this Sacred Sacrifice. Fortunately, His words are recorded for us in the Scriptures. Please read John 6:47-68. It will also be helpful to read: Matthew 26:26-28; Luke 22:19-20; Mark 14:22-24; and 1 Corinthians 10:16.

The Catechism of the Catholic Church is an excellent resource for learning more about the Catholic faith. Article Three in Part Two: "The Celebration of the Christian Mystery" contains a wealth of information. Please note, when you are looking for information in the *Catechism of the Catholic Church*, the paragraphs are numbered. The index will list the paragraph number (rather than the page number) of the highlighted topic.

There are many excellent books written about the Eucharist. Following are three that may serve as a wonderful starting place to learn more about Holy Communion: *The Lamb's Supper: The Mass as Heaven on Earth* by Dr. Scott Hahn; *7 Secrets of the Eucharist* by Vinny Flynn; and *Eucharistic Miracles: And Eucharistic Phenomena in the Lives of the Saints,* by Joan Carroll Cruz.

Finally, **the United States Conference of Catholic Bishops** has a website that offers a tremendous amount of information related to Catholic teaching. The web address is: www. usccb.org.

Acknowledgments

Mrs. Janet Bezdicek reviewed the manuscript offering insightful ideas. As a Catholic mother who is active in the Church, Janet has a heart for helping families live their faith more fully. It is a joy to work with her and an honor to call her friend.

Mr. Austin Duncan shared his artistic ability to create the illustrations for this book. As a Catholic high school student, Austin's talent is exceptional, and I am blessed that he shared his remarkable gift for this project.

Mr. Chris Kostelc carefully reviewed the manuscript offering excellent recommendations and a resounding endorsement. His suggestions improved the text greatly and I am both grateful and honored that he helped with this project. Chris has dedicated his life to teaching the youth and adults about our rich Catholic faith. He is a blessing to many, most especially me.

The well-known Catholic artist **Mr. Christopher Santer** oversaw the artwork of his student, Mr. Austin Duncan. As the art director at a Catholic high school, Mr. Santer combines his passion for art with his deep faith to teach young people about both. To learn about Mr. Santer's remarkable art work please go to: www.pacemstudio.com

Laura Spaeth is a graphic design genius who has patiently worked with me on a number of book projects. She is talented, caring, and a joy to work with. To learn more about her work please go to: www.telldesigns.com

Fr. Steve Ulrick shared his insights regarding Pope Francis while reviewing the letter from the Pope that is found within this text. Fr. Steve is a holy priest who exudes joy. What a blessing he is to our faith community, as well as to my family.

Fr. George Welzbacher served as Censor Librorum for this project. Fr. Welzbacher scrutinizes each word on every page making certain that the teachings of Holy Mother Church are expressed most faithfully. Through the multiple projects on which I have worked with Fr. Welzbacher, I have learned much from him and am so grateful for his patient teaching and his sincere care with each book.